Kamikaze Mouse, and other poems

Enjoy!

D Maupra

Kamikaze Mouse, and other poems

Duncan Thompson

Matador
9 Priory Business Park,
Wistow Road, Kibworth Beauchamp,
Leicestershire. LE8 0RX
Tel: 0116 279 2299
Email: books@troubador.co.uk
Web: www.troubador.co.uk/matador
Twitter: @matadorbooks

ISBN 978 1800464 353

British Library Cataloguing in Publication Data.
A catalogue record for this book is available from the British Library.

Printed and bound in Great Britain by 4edge Limited
Typeset in 11pt Baskerville by Troubador Publishing Ltd, Leicester, UK

Matador is an imprint of Troubador Publishing Ltd

This book is dedicated to all the wonderful children who helped inspire the poems in it.

Contents

Fabulous Family Poems

A Pot-Pourri of Poems

FOREWORD

I've been writing poems for a long time now, and I hope you enjoy reading them as much as I have enjoyed writing them. My poems mostly come from three different sources of inspiration, which I'd like to share with you in the hope that they might inspire you to write your own daft poetry.

Most of the poems come from funny or strange things which have happened or which I've seen during the day which just have to be written down. Poems in this book which were inspired like this include;

We Have a Problem with the Drone
There's a Wasp in my Trousers
Pigeon in the Playground
Camel with a Wonky Hump

Other poems come from something I've heard someone say, which instantly makes me think, 'that would make a great title for a poem'. Once you've got a title, the poem often just writes itself. Poems which started like this include;

Kamikaze Mouse
I'm Going to Close the School
I Wish I Was a Little Bird
I Drew a Smiley on My Hand

Sometimes when I have no ideas floating around, but want to write some poetry, I use random word generators to give me two words for a title. Often these just don't work out, but some poems in this book which came from that idea include;

Manhole Bandit
Basic Zebra
Camel Stoner
You Can't Put a Baby in a Lift

The rest of the ideas just seem to pop into my head, demanding to be written into existence.

Thanks to Grant Perkins for the awesome front cover and illustrations. Grant is a professional illustrator who has worked on WWE and Dr Who magazines among many other titles (check out his website at http://www.TheGrantPerkins.com). He can often be found lurking at comicons, and to have him illustrate my poems is a dream come true.

I really hope you enjoy this book, which is dedicated to the many weird and wonderful people I have worked with and taught over the years, not to mention my superbly odd family who have had to listen to these poems and pretend to like them for a long time now!

AWESOME ANIMAL POEMS

Kamikaze Mouse

I'm a kamikaze mouse and I feel no fear
I'll never go and hide when a cat is near.
I'll eat your cheese when you're in your bed
And do a mousey poo on your pet dog's head.

I'm a kamikaze mouse with mad ninja skills
And in your kitchen's where I get my thrills.
I don't eat crumbs from the greasy floor
I open up your fridge and eat cheese galore!

I'm a kamikaze mouse with a love of la fromage
While my mates are hiding in your garage
I'll be sneaking in your house and running free
And helping myself to the left-over brie.

I'm a kamikaze mouse and I'm never far away
I creep around at night and I sleep all day.
But don't bother moaning or chasing me, man -
I'm a kamikaze mouse and I don't give edam.

Camel with a Wonky Hump

There's a camel with a wonky hump
That lives at Chester Zoo
It flops about quite lazily
But why? I have no clue.

It has one hump that sits upright
And wobbles not at all
The other one lies flat and sad
While the first one stands up tall.

I do not know how come it broke
And ended up that shape
But I do know that fantastically
It was fixed with gaffer tape.

Playground at Night

In the park, when
The kids have done
The animals come
To have their fun.

Moles on a see-saw
Can't reach the floor
So Fox is lending
A helping paw.

Hedgehog swinging
Far too high
Perhaps his nose
Will touch the sky.

Bat and owls
Share the slide
Badger can't:
He's far too wide.

On the roundabout
Never slow
Round and round
The rabbits go.
In the park, when

The kids have done
The animals come
To have their fun.

They always share
They never fight,
Enjoying playing
All through the night.

Snake

Snake in the grass
Or is it a hose?
We went to find out
And it bit dad's toes.

Hose in the grass
Or is it a snake?
I'll give it a prod
With dad's garden rake.

Panda

Panda at the Zoo
Eating bamboo
Why don't you chew
Something new?

Make it you mission
Instead of just wishin'
A diet with fish in
Would have more nutrition.

You could try sprouts
Or a fillet of trout
But you won't I've no doubt
And so you'll die out.

Inside the Lion's Lunchbox

Inside the Lion's Lunchbox
If you're close enough to see
There's a wrapped up salad sandwich
And a flask of hot sweet tea.

A pack of cheese and onion crisps,
A chocolate bar or two
But what he'd really rather eat
Is me … or maybe you.

The only problem Lion has
Despite his razor claws
Is that he cannot open it
With his giant furry paws.

But if you go to help him out
And open up his dinner
Be ready for a running race
And make sure you're the winner.

There's a Wasp in My Trousers

There's a wasp in my trousers
So I'm standing very still
I don't want him to sting my leg
But I'm rather scared he will.

I don't know how he got down there
Or how to get him out
I'm trying hard to stay quite still
But I want to scream and shout.

I'd like to get him out of there
But I really don't know how.
Too late, the evil little thing
Has stung me: Ow, Ow OW!

Pigeon in the Playground

There's a pigeon in the playground, sir
And I think it might be dead.
Its wings are really floppy, sir
And there's maggots in its head.

Billy Jones has touched it sir,
With Harry's brand new pen.
He was trying to count the maggots, sir
He said there's more than ten.

I think a cat has killed it, sir
There's bite marks on its neck,
One of its legs is missing, sir
And its beak is just a wreck.

Now that's enough, I'm telling you
It's time to get in line
I'll go and get the caretaker
It's going to be just fine.

She'll go and fetch a plastic bag
And put the pigeon in
And give it a decent burial
In the non-recycling bin.

How Many Teeth Does a Crocodile Have?

How many teeth does a crocodile have?
It seems a large amount.
I really wouldn't like to be
So close that I could count.

A zookeeper some years ago
Got brave enough, and tried
To count those pointy gnashers
And the crocky opened wide.

She counted all the front ones
That make the scary grin
But couldn't see the back ones, so
She had to lean right in.

The last words she was heard to say
Were: "Ninety, ninety-one…"
When crocky snapped his jaws shut
And the zoo keeper was gone!

So I don't think I need to know
How many teeth he's got
As long as he is in his cage
And you and I are not.

Camel Stoner

I am a camel stoner
I keep them off the corn
It is a very boring job
You'll often hear me yawn.

If a camel tries to trespass
On the farmer's precious crop
A small and shiny pebble
Would be thrown to make him stop.

The reason that it's boring though
If you will just permit me
Is that there are no camels here
Because I live in Whitby.

Bird on a Lamp Post

Bird on a lamp post
Sitting there all regal.
I know you're not a pigeon.
But you're also not an eagle.

If I had my telescope
To get a decent look
I could tell what kind of bird you are:
A falcon or a rook.

A telephoto lens would help
Identify your breed
To know if you're a wren or finch
Is all I really need.

Bird on a lamppost
Not a crow or common seagull
You clearly think that you're all that
Just sitting there all regal.

Basic Zebra

What very few people know, as they sit in their safari
jeeps,
Or gaze through the bars at the city zoo
Is that the mono-chromed and stripy beast
They're looking at is just a basic zebra.

The zebra comes in many forms
Most of which are very shy:
The mottled hippoflechus has never been caught
By hunter's snare or camera
its most amazing detail being not the spots
on his back, but the fact they change colour at night,
like a walking disco.

A harder form to spot, is the verdant verdohippus
For his stripes are dark emerald
Against a coat of leafy green.
He walks freely on the grassy plains,
Safe from all predators in his camouflage.

But the hardest zebra of all to find
Is the genus equus perdu
No matter how close you get.
For the equus perdu, unique among mammals
Is vaporous and wraithlike... Invisible.

I Wish I Was a Little Bird

I wish I was a little bird
So I could fly up high
And see for miles and miles around
From way up in the sky.

I wish I was a little bird
So I could sing a song
So beautiful and tuneful that
You'd listen all day long.

But mainly if I was a bird
I'd dive and soar and swoop
And hover just above your head
To drop a massive poop.

SILLY SCHOOL POEMS

I'm Going to Close the School

'I'm going to close the school', he said
'I'm going to shut you down'.
'The lessons are too difficult, '
He muttered with a frown.

He pointed with his finger,
And with a solemn glare
Said, 'I'm going to sack you, too'.
And fixed me with his stare.

I waited quietly, then said,
'There's just one problem, son,
'You're not my boss, and furthermore
You're only in year one!'

Captain Curlytoes and the Early Years Kids

Have you heard the grisly tale
Of Captain Curlytoes?
The fiercest of the pirates,
As everybody knows.

He'd sailed on every ocean
And stolen tons of gold.
The tales of his adventures
Are the best that have been told.

He'd swum with sharks and jellyfish
And fought with swords and pistols
And in his mouth instead of teeth
Were diamonds, gold and crystals.

But even though he was so tough
His misdeeds have been ended
In an Early Years Class
He thought was undefended.

He was going to steal their glitter
And perhaps their glue supplies
But in the reading corner chair
He slowly closed his eyes…

When he woke up next morning
A crowd of little faces
Was staring at him angrily
From behind the tall bookcases.

He ran as fast as he could run
But they were so much fitter
They covered him in paint and glue
And heaps of coloured glitter.

His trousers were in tatters
And his shirt was ruined too
Two kids had grabbed his cutlass
And another nicked his shoe.

And so poor Captain Curlytoes
Hung up his Pirate Hat
And now lives in his cottage with
His parrot and his cat.

He still has bad dreams often
And the memories bring back tears
From when he was defeated
By the kids in Early Years.

If There Were SATs...

If there were SATs in awesomeness,
Or creativity,
Then you would all be Greater Depth
There is no doubt in me.

The SATs don't test resilience,
Or skills in sport or art.
But if they did you'd all fly high,
I know it in my heart.

SATs don't test your friendliness,
Or generosity,
But if they did, you all would pass
There is no doubt in me.

So just keep calm and try your best
On every SAT you do.
But know that they will only show
One tiny part of you.

The SATs don't test your awesomeness,
Or creativity,
But if they did you'd all fly high,
There is no doubt in me.

Captain Carrumbers is Rubbish With Numbers

Cuthbert Carrumbers is rubbish with numbers
And gets them mixed up all the time
From 1 up to 8, his knowledge is great
But he gets jumbled up after 9.

Vicky Vonsetters is no good at letters
Her spelling's as bad as can be
From A up to L, she knows it quite well
But she cannot sound out po-et-ry.

Darren DaPort is dreadful at sport
And can't even dribble a ball
He can't run too fast, and often comes last
And can't do gymnastics at all.

Robyn Reinhart is awful at art
Her pictures would all make you weep
She could draw a flower if given an hour
But her portraits you'd not want to keep.

It all would be cool, if they weren't at my school
And what makes the problem complex
Is that these poor creatures are all of my teachers
And the thing that they're bad at's their subject!

I Drew a Smiley on My Hand

I drew a smiley on my hand,
My teacher asked me why.
I couldn't think of anything
To give as a reply.

The other kids began to laugh
And sir got in a mood
He sent me to the Headteacher
For being very rude.

I showed the head the smiley
And he said, "Where do I start?
What lesson were you sitting in?
I guess it wasn't art."

I smiled and told him, "English, Sir."
And then he started yelling.
And when he stopped he stared and said
"Just go back to your spelling".

I drew a smiley on my hand
But I won't do that again.
The ink won't wash from off my skin
And my ears are still in pain.

Thinking Caps

I'm putting on my thinking cap
I'm turning on my brain.
My ears have been turned up to full
To help me learn again.

My eyes are facing forwards
And as focused as can be
I'm going to do my bestest work
Just you wait and see!

I'm putting on my thinking cap
And giving it a pat
The only problem is, I think
The batteries might be flat.

Nativity

Nativity, Nativity
Not all that it's cracked up to be.

The Teacher's pet dressed up as Mary
Mum's in the audience (she's quite scary)

Joseph forgetting what to say
Dropping the baby in the hay.

Angels with their halos wonky,
The grinning kid dressed as a donkey.

Nativity, Nativity
Not all that it's cracked up to be.

The friendly teacher on her knees,
Quietly saying 'louder please'.

A camel feeder, looking grumpy
Cardboard camels, not that hump-y.

A shining star who's looking sick
A wise man carrying a wrapped-up brick

Nativity, Nativity
Not all that it's cracked up to be.

Lots of parents looking proud
Finding their kiddie in the crowd.

Flicking through the pics they took
Putting hundreds on Facebook.

The start of Christmas, there's no doubt
That's what Nativity's all about.

FABULOUS FAMILY POEMS

Uncle Mark

Uncle Mark has a hobby
Which you may think is odd.
He likes to phone old people up
Pretending he is God.

He makes them do outrageous things
Like twerking in the bank.
Or stealing the piranhas
From the local zoo's fish tank

He even tricked the vicar once
He used a megaphone
And called to him at midnight
When he was sat at home.

He said 'ON MONDAY MORNING,
WHEN YOU'RE WALKING PAST THE SCHOOL
YOU MUST HOP ON JUST ONE LEG'
He did – he looked a fool!

He's very good at doing God
In fact, it's rather frightening
But I don't think that God is pleased:
Mark just got struck by lightning.

My Dad's a Composer

My Dad is a composer
And music's what he writes.
He writes it in the daytime
And he writes it when it's night.

But he doesn't write his music
For flutes or violins
He doesn't write for singers
Or for drums made out of tins.

The notes will not be followed
By a man with a guitar
Or played on fancy mandolins
Or even on sitars.

An orchestra will never play
The music he composes
Because my dad and his best friends
Make music with their noses.

They don't sound so amazing,
My dad and his best chums
But what is worse, they used to play
Dance music with their bums.

Aunty Sue

My Aunty Sue's a super-star
She drives around in an F1 car
She drives as if she's in a race
With a great big grin upon her face.

She likes to wrestle deadly snakes
When she's not making lemon cakes.
She flies a big hot air balloon
And once flew right up to the moon.

My Aunty Sue is pretty cool
Cos when she picks me up from school
She might be in a tank or train
Or even a boat in heavy rain.

She told me she worked as a spy
And I don't think that she would lie.
And when she worked for Scotland Yard
She was the Queen's main bodyguard.

My Aunty Sue once met a Yeti
And cooked it beans and boiled spaghetti
She took it back to Timbuktu
She promised me that it is true.

Although these things are really sick
My aunty's most amazing trick
Could beat the greatest human feats;
She never runs out of boiled sweets.

My Brother Bobby Picks His Nose

My brother Bobby picks his nose
It drives our mother mad.
She tells him it is dirty and
She tells him it is bad.

He'll pick it in the garden,
And he'll pick it in the car,
But the bogies that he picks at school
Are the biggest ones by far.

When he isn't hungry,
He saves them in a tin,
And when his belly's rumbling,
He devours them with a grin.

My brother Bobby picks his nose
Our mother thinks it's grotty
But at least his nose is always clear
And never, ever snotty.

My Mum

My mum, she bakes the sweetest cakes
And buns and biscuits too,
And there is nothing she can't make
With bits of card and glue.

My mum is great at homework
And helping pack my bags
And even when I'm naughty
She hardly ever nags.

When it is World Book Day
She makes me look so cool
Mine's the coolest costume
Of everyone in school.

My mum is just fantastic
And I think you ought to know
But even though I know it's true
I'd never tell her so.

A POT-POURRI OF POEMS

Does the Queen Eat Hotdogs?

Does the Queen eat hotdogs,
Or dip biscuits in her tea?
Does she swing like Tarzan
From her favourite garden tree?

Does she ever pick her nose
Or lick her soup bowl clean?
Does she stick her tongue out
When her maids are being mean?

I wonder if her majesty
Has cheated playing chess,
Or jumbled up the Prince's socks
And left them in a mess.

Has she pulled a wheelie
On a tricked out BMX
Or mixed some banging dance tunes
On a DJ's mixing decks?

Behaving properly all the time
Would surely be too tough
So sometimes even Queens
Must do some crazy stuff.

The Superhero Pill

A scientist has invented
A superhero pill.
And anyone who takes it
Will get a super-thrill.

It only lasts a single day
But it would be fantastic;
A whole day flying speedily
Or stretching like elastic.

Perhaps you'd be invisible
And play tricks on your mum
Or maybe x-ray vision
Could be a lot of fun!

You could be the bravest hero
And solve the hardest crimes
Or race Olympic athletes
Destroying all their times.

Super-strength could be quite good
For wrestling with your dad
Or maybe laser-eyeballs
Would not seem all that bad.

There's just one little problem
I have to say it's true
There is no superhero pill
So why not just be you.

We Have a Problem with the Drone

We have a problem with the drone,
It cannot fly no more
Possibly because it's stuck
Twelve feet above the floor.

I tried to land it on the ground
But it wanted to be free
And so it shot off to the left
And hit the tallest tree.

It's sat there hanging from a branch
Lights flicking red and blue
It really wasn't all my fault
I promise you it's true.

Don't worry though we have a plan
We think we know the trick
We'll just need a ladder and
A ten foot wooden stick.

We have a problem with the drone
But I am sure it will be fine.
It might be a little battered though
I'm glad it isn't mine.

Yorkshire Pudding

You can keep your fancy caviar
I don't want your posh bruschetta
I've never liked prawn cocktail
Or black olives served with feta.
You might like a vol au vent
Or salmon served on toast
Or maybe boiled quails' eggs
Are what you like the most.
But as far as I'm concerned my friend
There's nothing quite as good
When served with onion gravy
As an honest Yorkshire Pud!

Nasty Pasties

Nasty Pasties, 2 for a pound
With the worst ingredients to be found.

An elephant's toenail
Full of dirt
A muddy trainer
An Arsenal shirt.

Half a maggot
A badger's foot
A broken pencil,
Some coal and soot.

Mix them up, give them a grilling
Turn them into pasty filling.
Nasty Pasties, 2 for a pound
With the worst ingredients to be found.

A bogus tear from
A crocodile's eye
The second prize
From a coconut shy.

Some flaky skin
From grandad's heel
That white bit from
An orange peel.

Mix them up, give them a grilling
Turn them into pasty filling.
Nasty Pasties, 2 for a pound
With the worst ingredients to be found.

A flattened hedgehog
Peeled off the road
The top lip from
A female toad.

A pinch of salt
A scary mask
What else there is
I dare not ask.

Nasty Pasties, 2 for a pound
With the worst ingredients to be found.

I Have a Special TV Set

I have a special TV set
That no one else can see
It's in my imagination
And the programs are all free.

I can watch it when I'm in the car
And when I am at school
I can watch it at my grandmas
And in the swimming pool.

The programs that I like to watch
Are strange and rather fab
They feature talking animals
And unicorns that dab.

I love my special TV set
And take it everywhere
And best of all, I have to say
I never have to share.

Manhole Bandit

Manhole Bandit lies in wait
Listening to the footsteps of people
Walking home.

When he hears the steps
Of someone carrying doughnuts
He slowly lifts the manhole cover.

As they walk past, he grabs their ankle,
Hoping they will drop their bags
In fright.

If they do,
he steals just one doughnut,
And quickly lowers the cover.

The shopper will think they have tripped
And pick up their shopping.
Not knowing they are a doughnut short.

And in the sewer, the manhole bandit
Will sit, licking sugar from his lips.
Giggling.

You Can't Put a Baby in a Lift

You can't put a baby in a lift
He wouldn't reach to press
The button for the floor he needs
I've tried I must confess!

You can't have babies driving cars,
They're simply far too short,
To see over the steering wheel,
And so they can't be taught.

A baby cannot fly a plane
His brain is far too small
To land an airbus safely;
No, that wouldn't do at all.

A baby should not ride a bike
Though it would make him happy.
The seat would be quite painful as
It rubbed him through his nappy.

A baby should be left alone
To do what he should do
And that is eat and cry and smile
and most of all make poo.

Favourite Underpants

Crusty corners, gravy stains
The faintest smell of sprout
They're still my favourite underpants
What's all the fuss about?

The stitching's coming loose a bit
And the seams have got some dirt in
The elastic's got so baggy that
I have to tuck my shirt in.

They're getting pretty grubby
But I'm not a hygiene freak
They're not getting washed just yet
I'll take them off next week.

Chips on the Dodgems

Eating chips on the dodgems will never end well,
You'll always spill more than you eat
Your hair will be covered in ketchup and salt
And the grease will drip down on your seat.

Drinking slush on a pirate ship's only for fools
Especially if sat at the back
The people in front will be covered in ice
And will possibly try to attack.

Taking ice-cream on loop-the-loop's daft
And no-one would argue with that.
The ice-cream would surely soon fall from the cone
And end up as someone's new hat.

There's only one snack I would say that it's safe
To take on a white-knuckle ride
And that is pink candy-floss, sticky and sweet
It's the safest of snacks – I have tried.

It won't ever drop on a ride-goer's head,
Or fall from the stick in your hand.
And that's why the biggest queue will always be
The one at the candy-floss stand.

Epic Poet

There is no poem I cannot write
I write at least one poem a night.
My rhyming skills are truly epic
I think it might just be genetic.

Give me a title or first line
My poetry skills will start to shine.
No matter what the theme may be
it will not beat or challenge me.

I could write a poem on cats
Or dogs or mice or fish or rats.
I could write a poem on cakes
Or giant green man-eating snakes.

You could take two random words
Like 'helicopter' and 'lovebirds'
And I will weave poetic magic
With cool words in like 'camouflagic'*

There is no poem I cannot write
My rhyming skills are out of sight.
I could fill a book a month
And never, ever fail to … oh **

(* yes, it's a real word)   (** there are no words in the
English language which rhyme with month).